PARTY JOURNAL

This edition published by Parragon Books Ltd in 2014

Parragon Books Ltd
Chartist House
15–17 Trim Street
Bath BA1 1HA, UK
www.parragon.com

Written by Pollygeist Danescary

ISBN 978-1-4723-5980-3

Printed in China

MONSTER HIGH™

PARTY JOURNAL

PaRragon

Bath • New York • Cologne • Melbourne • Delhi
Hong Kong • Shenzhen • Singapore • Amsterdam

IT'S PARTY TIME!

It's time to party, Monster High style! Your ghoulfriends from Monster High have tricks and treats to help you throw all kinds of amazingly monstrous mashes. Skelebrate special events, birthdays and more with guides to creating your own fangtastic fashion, playing ghostly games and making spooky snacks.

Turn the page if you're ready to get your **monster party** on!

The Party of your Screams

Every ghoul loves a good party!
And any excuse to have a party
is a good excuse, whether you're
celebrating a special event,
turning Sweet 1600 or rewarding
yourself for an A in G-ogre-phy.

What is your favourite reason to have a party?

Baak Y to school

What are your three favourite party games?

SKEIDANCE Offict

Dare, Aght Truth or

dare, FS

What are the beast three songs to listen to at a party?

Boys iare song

when sa angry tikes a boy

Bad hah

Describe your most fangtastic fantasy party.
Where would it be? What decorations would you use?
What would you eat and drink? What games would
you play? Let your imagination go wild!

a   contest
party

PRETTY SCARY PARTY PREP

The first step to putting on a killer party of your own is laying the ghostly groundwork. When will your party be? How do you get your digs ready? What spooky skills should a good ghostess have? Read on to find out!

Parties

are so voltage! Getting together with all my ghoulfriends to do exciting new things (everything is exciting and new to me!) really zaps my bolts. When I feel like it's time for a party, the first thing I do is decide what I want to skelebrate!

What are some things you like to skelebrate?

What's your favourite event of the year?

What's the beast party you've been to?

Which of your ghoulfriends do you like to have parties with?

PRETTY SCARY PARTY PREP: SCARENTAL UNITS

Next, I ask my scarents when I can turn my dad's lab – aka the Fab! – into Party Central. To be really persvasive, I tell them why I want to have the party and what I'll do to help with preparations and clean-up.

Write a letter to your scarents telling them why you're so sparked about having a party and how you'll help out.

SCARENTAL UNITS: ENGAGE

Put your scarents to work!

Ask them to help make decorations, plan a menu, make snacks and organize party activities and games. Maybe you'll even learn something new about them! Try interviewing your scarents to see how they can help out.

INTERVIEW

What's the beast party you've ever thrown or attended? What made it spooktacular?

I Decay

_____

_____

What are your secret party skills?

I Decay

_____

What are your favourite party activities?

_____
_____
_____
_____
_____

Now that you've interviewed them, you and your scarents can list some ideas for how they can participate:

_____
_____
_____
_____
_____
_____
_____
_____
_____
_____

PRETTY SCARY PARTY PREP: INFRIGHTATIONS

Sending infrightations to all your ghoulfriends really sets the party mood. Which of your beasties will you invite?

Maul-bought
OR HOME-MADE?

Do you want to send maul-bought infrightations, fresh from the package and perfectly printed? Or would you prefer to make infrights of your own, each one a mini monsterpiece? Time to make a list of pros and cons!

Maul-bought

Pros:

Super professional.

Can add goregeous touches with the help of a little glue.

_____

_____

_____

Cons:

A bit less personal.

May not exactly match the party theme.

_____

_____

_____

HOMEMADE (ON THE COMPUTER OR BY HAND)

Pros:

Totally boo-nique.

Can be tailored to your party theme.

_____

_____

_____

Cons:

Time-consuming.

Might need to try different designs.

_____

_____

_____

INFRIGHTATION BASICS

The more formal the event, the earlier you should send out infrightations. Between fearleading practice, Dragonomics homework and family time, your ghoulfriends are *très* busy and you will need to give them enough time to plan. But even if it's a totally chilled-out *soirée*, try to send infrights out at least two weeks before the party if possible.

Do you want to use email or scale mail? It's up to you! It depends on the type of party you're throwing and how much time you have. Add some pros and cons to these lists....

EMAIL

Pros:
- Quick and easy.
- Oh soooo *moderne*.

_____
_____
_____

Cons:
- Not as elegant.
- Can't show off my penmanship skills.

_____
_____
_____

SCALE MAIL

Pros:
- Old-ghoul-style.
- Adds a personal touch.

_____
_____
_____

Cons:
- Takes longer to send.
- More work to make.

_____
_____
_____

What information do you need to include?

What are you celebrating?
_____

Day, date and time?
_____

Location?
_____

RSVP date?
_____

Appropriate attire (if applicable)?
_____

KEEPING UP YOUR DIGS

A good ghostess makes her ghoulfriends feel welcome by tidying up her digs. Make sure to check off everything on your cleaning list. And, of course, you should play some music and turn your cleaning session into a howling dance party!

SCREAM CLEANING

Once everything is spick and span, you can set up your party supplies, turning your digs into a monsterific party plaza!

- o Sweep up deadly dust bunnies.
- o Clean your dragon's litter tray.
- o Pick up things around the house.
- o Clean your room (or at least give anything messy to the monster in your closet).
- o Put away the dishes in the kitchen.
- o Don't forget yourself — take a beastly bath!
- o _____
- o _____

FANG TASTIC

GETTING IT PARTY-READY

o Set up a table with snacks and nibbles. If you're making any tasty treats in advance, be sure they're ready on time.

o Arrange your ghoulish games and activities area. Check to make sure all the supplies you might need are set out.

o Prep your pretty scary playlist.

o Put out your frightfully fabulous decorations! (This is the beast part!)

o _____
_____
_____
_____

HOWL ABOUT IT?

Draw your purrfect party set-up!

FREAKY-FAB PARTY SNACKS

At a party, you get to eat fun snacks that you don't have every day. Here are some party snack ideas. Add your own faves to the list!

- Pigs in shrouds
- Monsterella sticks
- Crisps and salsa dip
- Bat wings with hot sauce
- _____
- _____
- _____
- _____

FOOD RESTRICTIONS

There may be foods that some of your ghoulfriends can't eat.
(Draculavra's a vegetarian, so no pigs in shrouds for her!)

Ask your guests if there are any foods they can't eat so you
can have something for everyone. You can also find out their
favourites! Record your notes here for future reference:

Ghoulfriend: _____ Can't eat: _____ Loves to eat:_____
Ghoulfriend: _____ Can't eat: _____ Loves to eat:_____
Ghoulfriend: _____ Can't eat: _____ Loves to eat:_____
Ghoulfriend: _____ Can't eat: _____ Loves to eat:_____
Ghoulfriend: _____ Can't eat: _____ Loves to eat:_____
Ghoulfriend: _____ Can't eat: _____ Loves to eat:_____

When you're ready to go
shopping for ingredients,
remember to take this
list with you!

FREAKY FOOD SHOPPING LIST

_____
_____
_____
_____
_____
_____

De-fright-ful Decorations

Choosing party decorations is so exciting! You can make everything look so bonita if you use your imagination! You can use crêpe paper, streamers, balloons, card, papier mâché ... whatever you wish!

Jot down some freaky-fab decoration ideas!

Use the space below to sketch ideas for your party decorations.

Perfectly IMPERFECT

GHOSTESS ETIQUETTE

The most important thing to remember is that you want your ghoulfriends to have a wonderful time and feel comfortable *chez toi*. To make everyone feel *magnifique*, offer ghouls drinks as they arrive, introduce ghouls who haven't met each other and have a special place for ghouls to leave their coats, bags and iCoffins.

To welcome ghouls monster-party-style, make up a rock-solid greeting to say to them as they arrive. Write some greeting ideas below!

_____

_____

_____

_____

Remember to make your guests feel spooktacular during the party and your *fête* is sure to be a hit!

Let's get this scary-cool party started!

It's time to pick your freaktacular theme and get the party going with activities, games and more.

Be creative and party like a Scarisian! On the next page are some great ideas for skelebrating birthdays!

Bootiful Birthdays

Your birthday is your very own special event, so you should skelebrate in spookerific style. Whether it's with fab freshwater party games or monster makeovers, this will be a party to remember!

SWEET 1600th BIRTHDAY BASH

Electrifying

Nothing says 'birthday party' like a Sweet 1600th! Decorate the room with lots of pink and black and hearts, and get ready for the sweetest birthday party you've ever had! What would your perfect Sweet 1600th bash be like?

_____

_____

_____

_____

_____

_____

_____

_____

_____

_____

fangtastic presents

Birthday presents are the beast! We all love getting something new and exciting. Here are a few tips for opening them.

Start with the present closest to you. Don't pick through the pile — you'll get to open them all, don't worry! After you open each present, thank the ghoulfriend who gave it to you. Any present you get is a thoughtful gesture so be appreciative of your fangtastic friends. Once the party's over, write thank-you notes to your ghoulfriends for the gifts ... just like everyone did 1,600 years ago!

Draft some thank-you notes here!

Dear _____

_____

_____

_____

_____

_____

_____

Dear _____

_____

_____

_____

_____

_____

_____

Dear _____

_____

_____

_____

_____

_____

_____

Dear _____

_____

_____

_____

_____

_____

_____

Birthday Spooktacular!

Name some golden things that make you feel like a birthday queen!

_____

_____

_____

_____

_____

_____

_____

_____

_____

_____

A PARTY

A party that will make you say "Oh my ra" has got to have a killer playlist. Try these songs, and add some of your own.

"Call Me Mummy"

"Some Frights"

"What Makes You Bootiful"

DRESS LIKE A QUEEN

To be truly pharaonic, you need to dress like a pharaoh, which means it's time to be mummified. Divide into two teams for this preservation competition! (You'll need several rolls of toilet paper.)

Instructions:

1. Each team picks one ghoul to be the pharaoh. (If you play multiple rounds, you can take turns being the pharaoh.)

2. The pharaoh stands in the middle of her team.

3. On the count of three, each team has to mummify the pharaoh by wrapping her completely – except her face – in toilet paper!

4. The team that turns their pharaoh into a mummy first wins!

5. Whip out your iCoffins. You're going to want to preserve these images forever!

Draw your own versions of the mummy pictures you took here. You can try to recreate the pictures exactly or you can let your imagination go wild!

You
Can't
Keep
Royalty
Under
Wraps!

CREEPOVER BIRTHDAY PARTY

What could be better than an all-night birthday party? Stock up on some voltage snacks and monster makeover supplies, learn some secrets about your ghoulfriends and break out the sparky decorations, complete with black and white crêpe paper.
This birthday creepover will be one to scream about!

What are your favourite things to do at a creepover party?

_____

_____

_____

_____

_____

Who would you invite to spend a bolt-popping night at your Fab?

_____
_____
_____
_____
_____
_____

What's the most electrifying thing you've ever done at a creepover party?

_____
_____
_____
_____
_____
_____
_____
_____
_____

SCARYLICIOUS

CREEPERIFIC CUPCAKES

You'll definitely need something to keep your batteries charged all night long. So, prep some un-iced **cupcakes** before your ghoulfriends come over, then give the cupcakes **alternative** makeovers together. You'll need the un-iced cupcakes, white icing, food colouring, liquorice sticks, chocolate chips and other sweets for decorations, one bowl and spoon per ghoul and an icing bag (a bag with a metal or plastic tip).

Use your toppings to create **ghoul-ammed-up** cupcakes! Make different icing colours by mixing small amounts of the white icing with a drop or two of food colouring. Give your cupcakes hair, eyes, ears (with earrings!), noses, rosy cheeks and lipstick.

Draw some sweet designs for your ghoul-amorous cupcakes here!

Monster Makeovers

SKIN SCARE

You've got to take care of your skin, mate, if you want to keep it smooth and healthy after lots of outdoor hang time. Give your face a vibrant glow with a relaxing face mask. Put on some fintastic music and get out the cucumbers!

You'll need:

- daily cleanser
- 1 regular-sized tube of mud mask (should be enough for four ghouls)
- 1 cucumber, sliced

Instructions:

1. Make sure your hair is off your face. Ghouls with long hair should tie it back to keep it out of the way. Ghouls with shorter hair can clip it back or use a hairband.

2. To make sure the mud mask won't irritate anyone's skin, each ghoul should put some on her wrist and leave it there for at least 15 minutes, then wash it off. If any ghoul's skin shows signs of irritation, she should skip the mud mask. (But she can still use the cucumbers!)

3. Wash your face with the cleanser.

4. Apply the mud mask to your face (steering clear of the eyes) and set a timer for 20 minutes. Everyone's scales will be smooth and goregeous soon!

5. Lie down and place a slice of cucumber on each eye. This is a great time for a ghostly gossip session.

6. Remember to take lots of pictures of your ghostly mud-mask faces! When the timer goes off, throw away the cucumbers (definitely don't eat them!) and wash your face.

GHOULS RULE!!

What a goregeous glow!

What's a freaky-fab look you've been dying to try?

Get your ghoulfriends
to help you try it out!

SWAPPING MAUL!

Time for a freaky-fab
style update? Then get raiding
your ghoulfriends' wardrobes,
because one ghoul's 'done with this'
is another ghoul's 'can't wait
to wear it!'

Ask every ghoul to bring the clothes she doesn't want to wear
any more, pull out the full-length mirrors and set up some
snacks. It's a good idea to have a wish list prepared before
you start 'shopping'. What clawsome clothes would you really
like to score?

_____

_____

_____

What are some of your dream outfits? Include a mix
of clothes you already own and clothes you wish you had!

_____

_____

_____

MAUL PREP

When your ghoulfriends arrive, start by skimming through magazines like *Sevenscream*, *Teen Ghoul* and even *American Fearleader* and tearing out pages with clawsome outfits – the better to inspire you with!

SHOP UNTIL YOU DROP

Then throw all your unwanted clothes in a pile. Sort the clothes by type (trousers, shirts, skirts). Now pick out some new threads from the heap. You may have to haggle if you and another ghoul are eyeing the same piece!

Getting to Know Boo

You may think you know everything about your ghoulfriends, but there are probably a few facts that you've never even thought to ask about (or maybe you've forgotten them — remembering every little thing is like trying to hold on to a goldfish!) Here are some questions to get you started.

What's your favourite song to sing in the shower?
What is your freaky flaw?
What film do you know all the words to?
What's your favourite toothpaste flavour?

Now add some questions of your own:

_____

_____

_____

_____

'SWIMMING WITH THE FISHIES' PARTY

Hey, mate, for a sunny summer birthday bash, break out the screech towels, swimsuits and a few screech balls and you're ready for a fintastic time in the pool! Add some twinkly lights to the pool fence for a freshwater grotto effect and be prepared with ice scream and hamburgers – flapping your fins really works up an appetite!

Safety tip:
Ask an adult to stay nearby while you and your mates are in or around the pool!

Some of my favourite summer tunes are
Summer of Fishy-Nine, Summer Frights and
Itsy Bitsy Teenie Weenie Yellow Polkascare Bikini.
What are yours? Make a fishy party playlist!

Hey
Gills!

What fintastic water games can you play to keep cool, in the pool and out?

SO THIS CENTURY...

I GOT MAD SKILLS

Safe Skin in the Sun

SKIN-SCARE TOP TIPS:

Playing games in the pool is tons of fun, but it can be rough on your scales. You need to put skin scare first.

- Apply a waterproof sunscream.

- Stay hydrated! Drink lots of liquids, especially water. (But, uh, not pool water.)

- Don't stay in direct sunlight too long. Take a break and spend some time lounging under an umbrella or a covered area and chatting with your ghoulfriends.

- Pop on a hat if you've been out for a while. The skin on your face is extra-sensitive!

- Awfully important: even when it's cloudy out, the water in the pool reflects sunlight and you can burn more easily than when when you're away from the water. So reapply sunscream every hour no matter what!

While you're resting in the shade, take this quiz with your friends. Are you most like a vampire, a dragon or a sea monster? Find out!

1. Before you go anywhere, what do you check in the mirror?

a. Your outfit, to make sure it looks as creative as you feel.

b. Your skin, to confirm that you're moisturized.

c. Nothing – no mirror can truly reflect your beauty.

2. What is your favourite activity?

a. Painting, sewing, writing – you love to express yourself!

b. Swimming, playing football, playing casketball – sports make you feel great.

c. Shopping, experimenting with make-up, talking to your ghoulfriends – you love to pamper yourself and bond with your pals.

3. What is your dream howliday?

a. Going to Scaris to see all the gore-geous artwork.

b. Frolicking in the waves with your ghoulfriends on a Hexican beach. Blue waters as far as the eye can see!

c. Exploring Screamattle – quaint shopping, not too much sun and lots of relaxing.

Continued....

4. What do you look for in a beast friend?

a. Someone who is scary supportive.

b. Someone who loves to be active.

c. Someone who loves to talk on the phone all night!

5. What is your favorite subject in school (if you had to choose one!)?

a. Ghoulish literature.

b. Physical deaducation.

c. Biteology.

If you chose mostly As, you're most like a dragon! You're creative and love getting inspired by objects of beauty. Just be sure to make enough time for your ghoulfriends!

If you chose mostly Bs, you're most like a sea monster! You love to splish, splash and have a good time. Keep having fintastic fun, but add in some relaxing activities to strike a healthy balance.

If you chose mostly Cs, you're most like a vampire! You don't love the sun, but you do love spending time with your ghoulfriends and taking care of yourself. You may need to add a little room into your schedule for studying – but don't stop having a great time with your beasties!

heart-y tea birthday party

Tea and crumpets do a birthday ghoul good!

Vic-terror-ian Fangland was sooooo romantic.

When Queen Vic-terror-ia reigned in Fangland, they had parties just like in some of my favourite books, with live musicians, dancing and reciting of poetry by William Spooksfear, Ben Jekyllson and Sir Walterror Scott. Today, any Vic-terror-ian birthday shindig worth its fangs will come complete with teensy sandwiches, scarylicious scones and pots and pots of tea.

Get in the spirit by creating fancy Vic-terror-ian Fanglish names for you and your ghoulfriends. Here are some examples:

Lady Draculaura the Fourth
The Honourable Fearess Frankie Stein
Duchess Cleo of Egyptshire
Countess Clawdeen Wolf

k

7

Spooksfear Style

William Spooksfear is beast known for writing plays (hello, *Romeo and Ghouliet*), but he also wrote sonnets, which are a type of poem. Write some poems of your own as a group, using the opening lines opposite to get started.

1. Sit in a circle.
2. Ghoul A (the birthday ghoul!) reads the opening line, then makes up a line of her own that rhymes with it.
3. The ghoul to her left then makes up a rhyming line and so on around the circle.
4. Try not to repeat words, but don't worry if you do.
5. The poem can make sense, but it doesn't have to!
6. Once everyone has added a line, start over with a new opening line (and a new Ghoul A).

Here's an example:

♡ Opening line: We all go to Monster High.
♡ Ghoul A: We tell the truth; we never lie.
♡ Ghoul B: We like to snack on apple pie.
♡ Ghoul C: We like to laugh but not to cry.

Start off with one of these opening lines:

♡ I think I saw a little bat.
♡ Lagoona loves the big blue sea.
♡ The maul will have the perfect shop.
♡ Tie your fur up in a bow.
♡ Monsters rock. I think that's clear.
♡ We've got spirit; yes, we do.

Now write your own opening lines here.
Make sure to end with a word that
rhymes with a lot of other words:

SO THIS

CENTURY...

Heart-y Tea

A good tea party is about more than just bites to eat!
You should set the mood with some nice classical music.
(The soundtracks to Jane Austen films are a good choice.)
And visit some charity shops, craft shops and costume shops
to select some fangtastic accessories. Set the items out on
a table so you and your ghoulfriends can get dressed up
before you sit down to tea. You can also get some perfectly
mismatched teacups and saucers at the charity shop.

Accessory ideas:

★ freaky feather boas
★ chic hats
★ old-ghoul gloves
★ ghoul-amorous jewellery
★ lace handkerchiefs

TEA-TIQUETTE

Tea is a formal occasion, so be on your beast behaviour! Quick tips:

★ Milk and sugar should be on the table for each ghoul to add if she wants.

★ The teapot's spout should point towards the ghostess.

★ Don't clink your spoon against your teacup as you stir.

★ Leave your saucer on the table when you lift your teacup.

★ You may have heard otherwise, but here's the truth: to be truly skelegant, keep your pinkie in, not out!

The nibbles you serve at tea are monstrously important — and they're the perfect backdrop for bonding with your ghoulfriends. Every tea party should have bite-sized sandwiches, scones and desserts. Plan your heart-y teatime menu here!

WANNA GRAB A BITE?

SCARY Licious

To give your ghoulfriends the aristobatic treatment, you'll need to give them some scarylicious options for their tea-drinking. Take this quiz with your ghoulfriends to find out what flavour your tastebuds will like beast!

1. What is your dream pet?
a. Fiery dragon.
b. Nocturnal owl.
c. Wee woolly mammoth.
d. Cuddly bat.

2. What is your favourite perfume scent?
a. Something spicy and adventurous.
b. A flowery, romantic blend.
c. Something that smells cosy and comforting.
d. Sweet and soothing.

3. If you could have any career, what would it be?
a. Extreme athlete.
b. Wildlife biteologist.
c. Writer of ghoulish literature.
d. Scary-cool party planner.

4. What do you do after school?
a. Fearbook, casketball, fearleading, anything!
b. Ride my bike around the block.
c. Finish my Clawculus homework.
d. Talk to my ghoulfriends on my iCoffin.

5. What is your favourite snack?

a. Nuts (like pistachi-ghosts and peanuts).
b. Fruit (like scareberries and abominapples).
c. Anything chocolatey.
d. Cheese crackers.

If you chose mostly As, you should try Indian chai! You're adventurous and seek out the exciting things in unlife.

If you chose mostly Bs, you should try chamomile tea! You love to take in the goregeous nature all around you. Add a little honey to your tea, but no milk — that would dilute the sweet, flowery taste.

If you chose mostly Cs, you should try peppermint tea! You're a big fan of staying in on rainy days and getting lots of thinking time.

If you chose mostly Ds, you should try black vanilla tea! You're sweet, but not too sweet, and you love your ghoulfriends, but also enjoy spending time on your own. Add only a little bit of honey to your tea so you don't cover the warm vanilla flavour, and add some milk if you want it to be a little creamy.

FREAKY FLASHBACK TO THE '80s

BIRTHDAY PARTY

Blue eyeshadow, multiple pairs of socks, and neon leggings will take you and your ghoulfriends back in time to the '80s. Better yet, ask everyone to dress like Monsterdonna: black and white lace, scary-cool gloves and lots of necklaces! Hit charity shops for '80s movie posters, blast some '80s tunes and use neon colours everyscare. Neon pink and neon green are pretty vinelicious, if you ask me.

For true authenticity, your '80s party should be an iCoffin-free zone. Try to make it through a whole night without texting anyone!

Who knows all about the '80s? Your scarents, of course! Pump them for information about the decadent decade. You can also get the spooky-skinny from aunts, uncles, grandscarents — anyone who can remember life before the internet. Pick some interview subjects and ask them the questions below:

What '80s fashion did you love and what did you loathe?

What were your favourite '80s films and TV shows?

What about TV adverts? Do you remember any funny ones?

What was your favourite and least favourite '80s music?
Teach me your beast dance moves!

What board games and book crazes do you remember?

What were your favourite snacks?

No '80s party is complete without someone sporting a mullet. You are too spooktacular for that particular style, but you can subject a cut-out to it! (My own hair is much more plant-punk than a mullet, for the record.) You'll need a drawing or photo of someone with short hair in profile. You can find a photo, or you can draw someone yourself on a piece of thick card.

You and your ghoulfriends need to make some mullets! If your monster is blonde, use yellow wool; if brunette, use brown wool.

You'll need:

* ❋ 10 cm strips of paper
* ❋ 1 ball of wool
* ❋ 1 blindfold
* ❋ glue

1. Write your name on the back of your paper strip.
2. Cut the wool into 15 cm pieces and glue them onto your strip.

3. Allow the glue to dry, then place small pieces of tape on the back of your strip. (You're really going to tape your mullet, not pin it.)

4. Blindfold the first contestant. Turn her around in several circles. When you stop turning her, leave her facing the monster.

5. The contestant will stick her mullet to the poster where she thinks it should go. No touching the wall to try to work it out!
6. The ghoul with the closest mullet wins!

FRIGHTEOUS FILM MADNESS

Pick out an '80s film to watch to really take you back in time! Before the film starts, check out some of the adverts your scarents told you about when you interviewed them!

Films to watch:

★ The Breakfast Club
★ The Goonies
★ Labyrinth
★ The Princess Bride
★ Sixteen Candles

It's time for a party theme review! Which birthday party idea sounds like a total scream to you? Why? Write howl about it here:

FRIGHT ON

FANG TASTIC

Monster High

What totally voltage presents did you receive for your last birthday? Which ones meant the most to you and why?

GHOSTS OF BIRTHDAYS PAST

Did you have one birthday in particular when you were a small ghoul that was your favourite? Was it when you turned 15 days old or 1600 years old? Write everything you can remember about it and why it's so special to you here.

MONSTER
HIGH

GHOSTS OF BIRTHDAYS PAST

Be yourself
BE UNIQUE

Skelabration Parties

Skelebrate national and international special events in style! We've got monster tips for all kinds of skelebrations, from Scarisian to Hexican, patriotic to romantic and spooky to sparky. There's no party like a Monster High party!

Freaky FAB in Every Way

Friday the 13th Party

Skelebrate every Friday the 13th with your ghoulfriends! Decorate by setting out 13 of each item you choose (they can be anything — candles, abominapples, buttons) and invite 12 ghoulfriends over (plus you is 13!) to skelebrate all things 13.

As every monster knows, Friday the 13th is all about being lucky. When have you felt particularly lucky?

A guessing game that will have you dying of curiosity....

The 'answer ghoul' picks something from Monster High (a character, location or object — be creative!) and doesn't tell anyone what it is. The group gets 13 questions in total to guess the item, but they are only allowed to ask questions that can be answered 'yes' or 'no'. Remember to start with the question, **Monster, vegetable or mineral?** to narrow things down. (Another good question might be "Is it bigger than an icoffin?") After you've guessed (or reached 13 questions without guessing) the answer, it's someone else's turn to be the answer ghoul.

13 DANCES

Dance the lucky 13th away!
Put on your favourite lucky
music for a mini dance party.
Get in a big circle and take
turns dancing in the middle.
The ghouls in the circle should
copy whatever dance moves the
ghoul in the middle is doing.

Once all 13 ghouls have led a dance, see if
you can **remember all 13 dance moves**
in the right order!

Bonus points for anyone
who can do the Monster High
theme song dance!

SCAVENGER 13

Since 13 is such a lucky number, it's always good to gather items in sets of 13. This scavenger hunt can be played each ghoul for herself or in teams of two or more. Add your ow ideas below for items you need to find. The first ghoul (or team) to take pictures of 13 of the items is the winner!

- 🕸 Bolts (Frankie might need extras)
- 🕸 Mad science book
- 🕸 Potted plant
- 🕸 Moisturizer (Lagoona can always use some!)
- 🕸 A copy of *Teen Scream*
- 🕸 Musical instrument (so Operetta can play a tune)
- 🕸 Monarch butterfly (one of Skelita's pets!)
- 🕸 Clawdeen-worthy shoes
- 🕸 Sunglasses (just in case Deuce misplaces his)
- 🕸 Glasses (Can you find a style like Ghoulia's?)
- 🕸 Faux fur

Scary Cute

SCIENCE

Valentine's Day Spooktacular Party

What's pink, black, white and scary-cute all over?
A Valentine's Day Spooktacular, created especially
for me by Valentine himself! Serve up some pink
screamonade and pink sugar cookies, plus a tray
of raspberries, scareberries and grapefruit.
(You can drizzle the grapefruit with a little honey
if it's too tart for you.) Oh, and did I mention
that everything should be pink?

Now, Valentine's Day is a good time to think about boys,
naturally. Who are your secret special Valentines this year?
Write about them (and what makes them so special) here:

_____

_____

_____

_____

MONSTER MASH!

On Valentine's Day, you're simply dying to know what your future holds. A round of Monster MASH will give you a little glimpse!

MASH (Monster Mansion, Amoaning Apartment, Spooky Shack or Haunted House) will reveal fun fortunes, like where you'll live, who you'll marry, how many kids you'll have, what your job will be and what colour and kind of car you'll drive. It's a freaky sneak peek!

One ghoul will play the game at a time, but everyone will get a turn.

Fill in the chart below (there are more over the page). With your ghoulfriends' help, write down four things for each category: four people you might marry, four cars you might drive, four car colours, four places you might live and four jobs you might have. For 'number of kids' write 1, 2, 3 or 4.

Now, close your eyes and draw a spiral on a separate, blank piece of paper. When your ghoulfriends shout 'Stop!', count the number of lines in your spiral, from the top to the bottom. This is your MASH number!

Starting with the first item in your first category, count clockwise through the items on all of your lists. Cross out the item that you land on each time you count to your MASH number. When only one item is left in a category, circle it. Now you know your future!

M. A. S. M.

Married to

Monster cars

Car colours

Places to live

Careers

Number of kids

M.A.S.H.

Married to   **Monster cars**   Car colours

Places to live   Careers   **Number of kids**

M.A.S.H.

Married to   **Monster cars**   Car colours

Places to live   Careers   **Number of kids**

M.A.S.H.

Married to	Monster cars	Car colours

Places to live	Careers	Number of kids

M.A.S.H.

Married to	Monster cars	Car colours

Places to live	Careers	Number of kids

Hearts on (Jina) Fire

Make some clawsome hearts to give to your friends and relatives!

MONSTER HIGH

You'll need:

♡ crayons (used)
♡ silicone heart-shaped moulds

Heart
instructions:

1. With an adult's help, preheat your oven to 135°C.

2. Set one box of crayons aside to use for gift tags.

3. Gather all the ghouls together to peel the paper off the rest of the crayons.

4. Break each crayon into three or four pieces.

5. Place several crayon pieces (about a crayon's worth) into each mould.

6. You can make solid-coloured hearts or mix up the colours. But if you use too many colours in one mould, they'll blend together, so stick to two or three colours at the most.

7. With an adult's help, bake the hearts for 10 to 12 minutes.

8. Allow to cool and set. Once they're cool, pop them out of the moulds!

Who will you give
your hearts to?

_____
_____
_____
_____
_____
_____
_____
_____
_____
_____
_____
_____
_____
_____
_____
_____
_____
_____
_____
_____

GREEN SCENE: EARTH DAY PARTY

Help keep Venus's vined friends all over the world in tip-top shape with this pollen-tastic party. Drape the room in green, green and more green — preferably recycled — decorations and have a freaky-fab time.

Check out these oxygen-erific reasons for skelebrating Earth and add some reasons of your own....

✳ The planet provides us with goregeous
   natural scenery to look at and enjoy.

✳ Delicious fresh food and clean water come
   from the world around us.

✳ Some natural resources, like trees, are renewable.
   Planting enough trees helps regulate the amount
   of carbon dioxide in the atmosphere.

✳ Other natural resources, like petroleum,
   aren't renewable. Limiting our use of them
   makes them last longer.

✳ Using recycled paper products can help make sure
   that animals like Chewy and Sir Hoots A Lot
   and their wild-animal cousins have places to live.

✳ Conserving energy can help stop the polar ice
   caps from melting so the polar bears and other
   cold-weather animals won't become extinct.

KEEP IT GREEN

HOWL ABOUT IT?

Getting down with nature is the beast! Draw your own vinetastic garden hideaway here.

Scary Cute

FREAKY-CHIC FLOWERS

Plant your own temporary garden with another snack: flowers! Because sometimes it's okay to play with your food ... and create a garden of ideas for your next veggie snack attack.

You'll need cucumber slices, fresh spinach leaves, cherry tomatoes, baby carrots, celery sticks, radish slices and dip. And don't forget to find a big plate to use as your 'canvas'.

Go crazy! Use the veggies to design gardenscapes, boo-quets, flowers with Monster High ghouls' faces ... whatever comes to mind. You can work together on a big flower mural or you can each make your own mini monsterpiece.

Take a picture of your creations, then eat the veggies with the yummy dip.

HIDE AND SCREECH

Conserve some energy with a game of hide and screech ... in the dark! The more energy you save, the better off plants and animals are.

Instructions:

1. Turn off every light in the house and close all the curtains. Pick a ghoul to be the screecher. She'll start the game at the haunted base.

2. While the screecher counts to ten, all the other ghouls should hide.

3. When the screecher says, "Ready or not, here I creep!" make sure you're hidden. The screecher's job is to find all the hidden ghouls. The ghouls can try to reach the haunted base without getting caught or they can just hope the screecher doesn't find them.

4. The round is over when the last ghoul is found or reaches the haunted base.

5. The first ghoul to be caught by the screecher becomes the screecher for the next round!

Hexican Fiesta

Break out the red, white and green for a Hexican fiesta! Serve up some casketdillas and brush up on your español! Practise these words and phrases with your ghoulfriends!

English	Spanish
Hello!	¡Hola!
How are you?	¿Cómo estás?
I'm fine, thanks. And you?	Bien gracias. ¿Y tú?
What's your name?	¿Cómo te llamas?
My name is ...	Me llamo ...
Good morning	¡Buenos días!
Good afternoon	¡Buenas tardes!
Goodnight	¡Buenas noches!
Goodbye	¡Adiós!
Cheers	¡Salud!
Have a nice day!	¡Que pase un buen día!
I don't understand	No entiendo / No comprendo
A little	Un poco
How much is this?	¿Cuánto cuesta?

MONSTER HIGH.

HEXICAN HAT DANCE

Do some *bonita* dancing with your very own Hexican hat dance to skelebrate Hexican scaritage. Before your party, cue up some Hexican hat dance videos to give you some choreography ideas.

Hat Dance Tips:

- Break up into pairs and choreograph duets.
- Include a slow opening, then leap into quicker action.
- Choreograph in counts of four.
- Make sure to incorporate some twirls.
- Don't forget the footwork! Lots of heel-toe action goes into a good hat dance.

PARTY PREP: CASKETDILLAS

Cheesy casketdillas will fill up a whole crowd of skeletons! These have to be served hot, so you'll need an adult's help. You can make them before the party, then simply heat them up just before eating; or you can have everything prepared and cook them during the party.

You'll need (for two ghouls):

- ★ butter or cooking oil
- ★ 2 large flour tortillas
- ★ 100g grated Cheddar cheese
- ★ 225g chopped, cooked chicken (optional)
- ★ salsa dip
- ★ sour cream (to serve)

Instructions:

1. In a frying pan large enough for a tortilla to lie flat, heat the butter or oil so that the entire bottom of the pan is greased.

2. Place one tortilla in the pan on low to medium heat and allow to brown slightly. Set this tortilla aside.

3. Place the second tortilla in the pan. Immediately sprinkle the grated cheese over the tortilla. If you're using chicken, scatter the chicken on top of the cheese.

4. Place the first tortilla on top of the cheese, browned side up.

5. Press the tortillas together with a spatula.

6. Fry until the cheese is melted, then remove from the pan. Cut into wedges like a pizza.

7. Serve salsa and sour cream on the side.

HEXICAN HANDBAGS

Using bright fabrics and ghostly skills, sew your very own handbag — complete with some skelegant embroidery. Be unique!

You'll need:

- thick, bright fabric in various patterns and colours (scraps or new)
- colourful wool
- bright ribbon
- wool needle
- scissors
- tape measure
- pins
- white embroidery thread
- embroidery needle

1. Choose some fabric that you like and lay it out so you have two pieces that are 20 cm x 15 cm. These will be the sides of your bag. Each side can be made up of a single piece of fabric or multiple pieces layered together.

2. If your sides have multiple pieces, you'll use wool and a wool needle to stitch the pieces together.

3. To stitch the pieces together, first tie a knot in one end of the wool, then thread the other end through the wool needle. Holding the two fabric pieces you're sewing together with their edges overlapping, push the needle up from the wrong side of the fabric to the right side, with the needle going through both pieces of fabric. Then bring the wool down 3 mm away, through both pieces of fabric. Keep doing this until the pieces are stitched together.

4. When the pieces are assembled, place the two sides together, right sides facing each other. Pin the sides so the edges are lined up.

5. Using the wool and yarn needle again, stitch the 20 cm edges together; then stitch just one of the 15 cm edges together. Remove the pins.

6. Now make the handle! Cut a piece of ribbon to the desired length and stitch it to both sides of the opening of your bag.

7. Turn the bag the right way out.

8. Using the embroidery needle and the white embroidery thread, stitch a simple heart shape in the centre of one side of the bag. To do this, use medium-size stitches to outline a heart, then use stitches of varying lengths to create a 'scribble' effect inside the heart.

Design your own custom Hexican handbag here.
If you're feeling *muy* brave, break out the craft
supplies and make your bag come to unlife.
It's a limited edition!

MONSTER HIGH

SCARISIAN FLING PARTY

According to paragraph 7.14 of the Gargoyle Code of Ethics, it is a gargoyle's responsibility to throw a clawsome Scarisian Fling at least once a century.

Lay out a *très chic* spread of croissants, *chocolats* and sparkling grape juice, and add the red, white and blue of the French flag. *Vive la France!*

Ghoul LA LA!

VOCABU-SCARY

You need to learn un petit peu de français to skelebrate properly. Use the pronunciation guide below to sound out the phrases, then practise saying them with your ghoulfriends.

Yes	*Oui*	(WHEE)
No	*Non*	(NON)
Maybe	*Peut-être*	(puh-TEH-truh)
Where are the bathrooms?	*Où sont les toilettes?*	(OOH sawnt LAY twah-LET)
How much does that cost?	*Combien ça coûte?*	(COM-bee-an sah COOT)
That's adorable!	*C'est adorable!*	(say TA-doh-RAH-bluh)
What a surprise!	*Quelle surprise!*	(KELL sir-PREEZE)
A little bit	*Un petit peu*	(unh PUH-tee PUH)

What frightfully fabulous new adventures would you and your ghoulfriends have on a dream trip to Scaris? What sights would you see and what would you eat?

Scary Cute

SO THIS CENTURY...

I GOT MAD SKILLS

HOWLOWEEN PARTY

Get your digs ghoul-ammed up for a spooktacular Howloween! Old-fashioned Howloween decorations? So bland! Make everything new again by using craft supplies you have on hand to create your own ghoul-amorous Howloween decorations with some well-placed accessories.

First, add to this list of standard decorations:

x pumpkins x _____

x ghosts x _____

x bats x _____

x witches x _____

x cobwebs x _____

Then, add to this list of fangtastic accessories:

- ✗ hair bows
- ✗ bags
- ✗ zips
- ✗ safety pins
- ✗ purple eyes

- ✗ pink lips
- ✗ lashes
- ✗ _____
- ✗ _____
- ✗ _____

Next, gather your craft supplies:

- ✗ card in pink, black, white, orange or other scary-cool colours
- ✗ glue
- ✗ markers

- ✗ scissors
- ✗ ribbons (for hair bows)

Instructions:

1. Pick an item from the decorations list, like the pumpkin. Draw the pumpkin and cut it out.

2. Choose some items from the accessories and details list, like purple eyes and a bag. Draw these, cut them out, then glue them onto the pumpkin.

3. Repeat steps one and two with different combinations!

You can do this before the party or you can wait until your ghoulfriends arrive and create the decorations together!

HOWLOWEEN CHIC

CLAW some!

Before your ghoulfriends arrive, you need to get dolled up in a fangtastic Howloween costume. Will you be scary or will you be scary-cute? You have a lot of options!

Costume ideas:
- Fave Monster High Ghoul
- Casketball Player
- Fave Monster High Pet
- A Monster High Fearleader

What costumes do you think your ghoulfriends will wear? Why do you think each ghoul will make that choice?

PaRTY TiLL THE fuLL MOON COMES uP.

Get your body moving like you're in a *Dead Fast* comic with a fangtastic relay race, Howloween style. You'll need two pumpkins and some superhero reflexes.

Scary Cute ♥

How to play:

1. Divide into two even teams and line up facing forwards (so that each ghoul is looking at the back of the ghoul in front of her). Ghoul A (the first ghoul in line) on each team starts out with her team's pumpkin.

2. Ghoul A passes the pumpkin over her head to Ghoul B. Ghoul B passes the pumpkin under her legs to Ghoul C.

3. Repeat this over/under pattern until the pumpkin reaches the last ghoul in line.

4. The last ghoul runs to the front of the line with the pumpkin and passes it back in the same way, until each ghoul has been at the front of the line.

5. Whichever team gets the original Ghoul A back to the front of the line first, wins!

That was exhausting!

Monster High

What's the spookiest party you've ever been to?

Super
spooky!

OTHER FREAKY-FAB EVENTS

Did you get a new pet? Is it time for a fashion show? Did you get a surprise day off school? All of these freaky-fab occasions call for a spooktacular party! Any reason for a party is a good reason!

**Roll out the red carpet
for your ghoul-amorous
self and your GFFs!**

The polter-azzi (aka your
scarents) will snap pics
as everyone arrives in their
beast ensembles and then
it's party time. You'll want
red and gold decorations plus
ghoul-amorous photos of
your favourite stars adorning
the walls. Serve elegant
finger foods and ask your
ghoulfriends to arrive in
their red-carpet finest.

The Freakademy Awards have been
given since 1929, so there's a
long history of ghoul-amorousness
to live up to.

STARGAZING

When you're getting ghoul-ammed up for the party, you may want to use some of your favourite skelebrities as inspiration. Who are some creepy-cool actors you admire?

Some examples:
Skelena Gomez
Zac Efright
Anne Hauntaway
Robert Phantomson
Ghoulia Roberts
Jenniscare Lawrence

CHIC CHARADES

Before the Freakademy votes, you'll want to show off your fangtastic acting skills. Play a few rounds of charades to prove you've got what it takes!

Instructions:

1. Divide into two teams. Each team writes titles of books, skelevision shows or films, names of famous people or common phrases or quotes on slips of paper and then folds them up. Each team then places their slips in a separate bowl.

2. The teams take turns, with one ghoul playing the actor at a time. The actor picks a slip of paper from the other team's bowl. Don't tell anyone what it says! Without speaking, the actor helps her team guess her word(s) by giving signals using appropriate gestures (see opposite page!). She has three minutes (set a timer on your iCoffin).

3. The turn is over when the team guesses the title or the time runs out, whichever happens first. No guesses from the other team are allowed!

4. The team with the most correct answers wins.

★ **Book title:** Put your hands together then open them like a book.

★ **Film title:** Make an O with one hand to indicate a lens while cranking the other hand as if you are operating an old-fashioned film camera.

★ **Skelevision show:** Make a box with your fingers.

★ **Quotes and phrases:** Make air quotes.

★ **Famous person:** Pose with your hands on your hips.

Word hints:

★ Pull on your ear to indicate that the word being guessed sounds like the word you are about to demonstrate.

★ Pinch or open your thumb and forefinger for a short or long word.

★ Use your fingers to show the number of words in the answer; then use your fingers to show which word you want your teammates to guess.

★ Hold fingers against your arm to show how many syllables are in a particular word.

★ Show that a word guessed is correct by tapping your index finger on your nose.

★ Wipe your hand across your forehead when the ghouls on your team are getting hot (close to the answer) or cross your arms and shiver when they're getting cold!

Obviously, the highlight of the Freakademy Awards — after the fashion, the ghoulossip and more of the fashion — is finding out who wins each award! Pick a host to amp you up — this can be a ghoul, a guest, a scarent or an obedient sibling. Let the ceremony commence!

First, you need to create some awards.
Add to this list of award ideas!

Beast Spooktress

Beast Deadrector

Beast Costume Design

_____

_____

_____

Make frightfully fancy award certificates on your computer!

When you're ready for the ceremony, ask your ghoulfriends to write their names on identical slips of paper. Fold the slips in half and drop them in a hat.

The host will open the ceremony with a speech. Watch some award intros on BooTube for inspiration and write a speech for your host here:

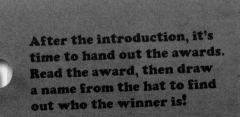

After the introduction, it's time to hand out the awards. Read the award, then draw a name from the hat to find out who the winner is!

Finish off with a Freakademy Award
viewing party. Make a list of films
that you consider award-worthy.
To work out which film you'll watch,
just put it to the vote!

Nominated films:

Monster Pet Party

Pets are monsters too! Skelebrate them in style, decorating with paw prints, pet pics and pet toys. And you can serve snacks in (new and unused) pet food dishes!

GHOULFRIEND TREATS

Make some easy snacks before the party so your ghoulfriends don't miss their feeding time. Try making this fur-and-feathers treat!

PUPPY CHOW

Puppy chow will fill you with puppy love! You'll need to refrigerate this for at least a few hours, so leave plenty of time before your party.

You'll need:

- 250g peanut butter
- 340g chocolate chips
- 110g margarine
- 1 box cereal (the latticed shredded wheat type)
- 275g icing sugar
- 1 clean paper bag
- Greaseproof paper

Instructions:

1. Put the peanut butter, chocolate chips and margarine in a bowl and microwave on high for 2 minutes (or until melted).
2. Pour the mixture over the cereal in a bowl and mix well.
3. Put the icing sugar in a paper bag, add the cereal mixture and shake it vigorously.
4. Spread the mixture on a baking tray covered with greaseproof paper and allow to cool.
5. Refrigerate to harden, then enjoy!

PARTY WITH YOUR PETS!

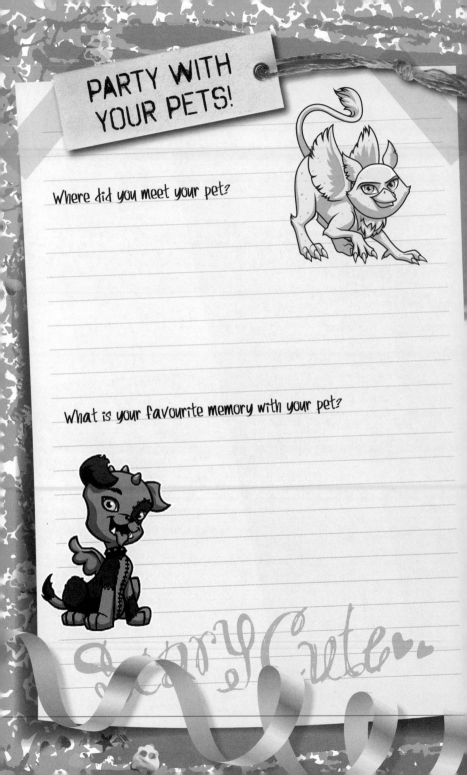

Where did you meet your pet?

What is your favourite memory with your pet?

What do you like beast about your pet?

_____

_____

_____

_____

_____

_____

If your pet could talk, what would they say to you?

_____

_____

_____

_____

_____

_____

_____

_____

_____

BooTube

Before the party, plug yourself into the internet and cue up the scary-cutest pet videos you can find. Try searches for some of these animals:

★ sloth
★ loris
★ kitten

★ baby goat
★ puppy
★ red panda

Jot down the names of your favourite videos here:

★
★
★

Now search for these duos:
★ horse and cat
★ bear and dog
★ hamster and cat

GHOST PET

If you've always wanted a pet but can't have one, or if you have one and want it to have a friend, this is your chance! It's time for you to adopt a ghost pet! What kinds of pets would you like to have?

★ dragon
★ snake
★ gargoyle

★ owl
★ ferret

FANGTASTIC PET BOOK

Fill out this fangtastic pet book for easy access to your monster pet's personal info.

To show off your pet's boo-nique nature, you'll need:

★ pictures of your pet
★ animal stickers
★ crayons and pencils

★ glue
★ scissors

PHOTOGENIC FAUNA

Stick photos of your pet's scary-cute mugs here!
Draw thought bubbles to capture their secret musings
and use stickers and crayons to decorate the page.

Monster High

How old was your fuzzy friend when you met them?

How much do they weigh?

How would you describe what they look like?

What cute things did they do as a baby?

What is their favourite game?

What does their bark, miaow, squawk or roar sound like?

Who are their favourite monsters and normies? Why?

What else is important to you about your pet?

FREAKY-CHIC FASHION-SHOW PARTY

Show off your couture with a fashionable extravaganza. Drape your tables with folds of freaky-chic fabric and fill vases with ribbons, lace and feathers. Top it off with some fashion mags scattered about artfully.

Some fashions, like little black dresses and pearls, are classic. Others are flashes in the pan. Opaque tights ... as trousers? Old-timey monsterstaches ... in the 12th century? Wearing a dress ... made of meat? None of these trends will last. What are some of the funniest fashion no-nos you can think of?

INSPIRATION

Get inspired by fashion magazines and websites. Look at fashion pictures, but also look at food, nature, sports ... even adverts. Each ghoul should write or draw her favourite ideas, then show them off to the group. Vote on the most creative, the weirdest and the ghouliest. Use this page to fill in some of your own inspirations.

ARTIST, MONSTER, CLAY

Work together to make a monster sculpture with this clawsome game. You don't need any supplies for it!

Instructions:

1. Break into groups of three. (If anyone is left out, some ghouls can go twice.)

2. One group of three stands up; everyone else stays seated as the spooktators. One ghoul is the artist, one is the monster and one is the piece of clay.

3. The clay faces the spooktators. It's very important that she never sees the monster!

4. The monster stands behind the artist and picks a pose (sitting, standing, kneeling, legs and arms straight, bent, crossed – be creative, but pick a pose you can hold for two or three minutes).

5. The artist sculpts the clay into the same pose the monster is in. The artist cannot speak, mimic the monster's pose or touch the clay. She should treat the clay as though the clay is an actual lump of clay or a block of marble, pushing and pulling and shaping the clay into the right shape, but without actually touching it! See how close you can get to matching the monster's pose!

6. Set a timer for three minutes. When the time is up, take a picture of the clay and the monster so you can compare them!

FREAKY-CHIC FASHION SHOW

To prep for your fashion show, pull some outfits from your wardrobe. You can take fashion in a gazillion directions. Try some of these ideas and then sketch more.

- monochromatic (one colour, head to claw)
- each piece a different colour
- clashing patterns
- baggy bottoms with fitted tops
- fitted bottoms with baggy tops
- as many layers as you can manage

MONSTER HIGH

FREAKY-CHIC
FASHION SHOW

Ask your ghoulfriends to bring their most
skelacious wardrobe pieces (tops, skirts, shoes, boas, jewels)
then add your own. After you've pooled it all together, put on
skella-cool, totally boo-nique, unexpected ensembles. Pick a killer
soundtrack, strut down the runway and then do it all over again!

Make a list of the songs you want to listen to.
Rolling in the Creep
What Makes You Boo-tiful
One More Fright

FASHION SHOW TIPS

💀 Lay some ribbon out on the floor to outline the runway.

💀 Blast out your clawsome soundtrack.

💀 Be each other's spooktators — break into two groups. One group will watch while the other group lines up to take turns strutting down the catwalk. Then switch.

💀 Walk the runway one ghoul at a time. When you get to the end, strike a pose and wait for the applause to die down. Then execute a graceful turn and stroll elegantly back up the runway.

'Mad Science in the Fab' Party

Living in the Fab is totally voltage: mad fashion plus mad science! Deck your house out like a glittery science lab, complete with beakers and lab coats, and set out some minty green desserts. Albert Frightstein and Marie Cursie would be proud!

FREAKY FAB

THE GHOSTLY FLOAT EXPERIMENT

You'll need:

- water
- sea salt
- a tall drinking glass
- 1 egg
- 1 small sachet each of ketchup, mustard and soy sauce

Instructions:

1. Pour water into the glass until it is about half full.
2. Stir in about six tablespoons of salt.
3. Carefully pour in plain water until the glass is nearly full. Don't disturb or mix the salt water with the plain water.
4. Gently lower the egg into the water.

What just happened? Well, salt water is denser than fresh water and objects float better in denser liquids. When you lower the egg into the liquid, it drops through the normal tap water until it reaches the salty water, at which point the water is dense en___ for the egg to float. Now try some experiments with this ___ the packets of ketchup, mustard and soy sauce float ___ eights? Does changing the water temperature have ___ ord your fright-dings here:

Variable:

Result:

Notes:

Variable:

Result:

Notes:

Variable:

Result:

Notes:

Variable:

Result:

Notes:

POLTER-PENNIES EXPERIMENT

Divide into groups of a few ghouls each and test your powers of deaduction with this polter-pennies experiment.

You'll need:

- ★ 10 x pennies (not shiny)
- ★ 10 x 2p pieces
- ★ 10 x 5p pieces
- ★ 10 x 10p pieces
- ★ several nuts and bolts
- ★ 60ml white vinegar
- ★ 60ml orange juice
- ★ 60ml lemon juice
- ★ 1 teaspoon salt
- ★ non-metal bowl
- ★ paper towels

$\{m+h\}$

Polter-Penny Demonstration 1:

1. Pour the vinegar into the bowl, add the salt and stir.
2. Put five pennies in the bowl and slowly count to ten.
3. Take out the pennies and rinse them in some water.
4. Are they shiny and clean?

What just happened? Vinegar contains acid and the acid in the vinegar reacts with the salt to remove the copper oxide that was making your pennies so uggo.

Polter-Penny Demonstration 2:

1. Put five more pennies in the bowl and slowly count to ten.
2. Take them out but don't rinse them. Place them on a paper towel to dry.
3. Wait long enough and the pennies will turn bluish green because malachite, a chemical, will form!

Polter-Penny Demonstration 3

1. Put the nuts and bolts in the vinegar you just used.
2. They may turn copper because the vinegar removed some of the copper from the pennies. The copper will then be attracted to the metal in the nuts and bolts.

Polter-Penny: Further Experiments

Now you know what happens when you put dirty pennies in a salt-and-vinegar solution. But what would happen if you change some of the variables?

1. Try the above again with other acidic liquids, like lemon juice or orange juice.
2. Try it with the other coins you found.
3. Try changing the amount of salt you added.

Record your observations on the next page!

Variable:
Result:
Notes:

Variable:
Result:
Notes:

Variable:
Result:
Notes:

Variable:
Result:
Notes:

Variable:

Result:

Notes:

Variable:

Result:

Notes:

Variable:

Result:

Notes:

Variable:

Result:

Notes:

FEARBOOK MEETING PARTY

When the school year starts wrapping up, you know what that means ... it's time to call a fearbook meeting, ghouls! Get the sports, gossip, clubs and photography staff members together to create a fearbook that will put all the fearbooks in the history of Monster High to shame.

Fearbooks help you revisit all the things that happened over the past year. What are some of your favourite things about fearbooks?

Did your school create fearbooks? If so, look back through them. What spooktacular memories do your old fearbooks trigger?

What things are different now than they were in your old fearbooks?

PHARAOH'S PHOTO BOOTH

Come to the party picture-ready and take some pharaohific on-the-spot fearbook pics in the photo booth.

You'll need:

★ several different patterned cloths or papers for backgrounds (tartan, polka dots and stars are all great choices)

★ camera

★ colour printer and photo paper

Oh My Rah

**You'll also need photo booth props!
Try some of the props below and
add some of your own to the list.**

Props:

- ★ tiara
- ★ wand
- ★ pom—poms
- ★ sports equipment
- ★ schoolbooks or binders
- ★ stuffed animals
- ★ garden gnome
- ★ cauldron
- ★ beakers
- ★ feather boas
- ★ capes

★ _____
★ _____
★ _____
★ _____
★ _____
★ _____
★ _____
★ _____
★ _____
★ _____
★ _____

Now jump into the photo
booth solo or in groups,
trick yourselves out with
props and snap away!
Pick your favourite pics
to print out.

The most important way to leave your mark on the fearbook is by designing a ghoul-amorous cover. Try out some fur-rocious cover designs here!

Game Fright Party

Break out the cards and board games! Decorate in red and black and scatter some red and black playing cards on the tables to match. Board games and card games are often beast for four players, so you will probably want to invite either three friends and all play together or seven friends and play in groups of four.

MONSTER HIGH

Whether it's a game of skill or a game of chance — or a combination of both — card and board games are a scary-fun way to hexercise your brain. What are some of your favourite games to play?

_____

_____

_____

_____

_____

_____

_____

_____

_____

_____

_____

_____

JACK(SON) SNAP

 **Instructions:**

1. Deal the whole deck of cards, face down. Don't look at your cards – they stay face down throughout.

2. The ghoul to the dealer's left turns the card on top of her stack face up in the centre of the table.

3. Play continues with ghouls placing their cards face up in the centre of the table.

4. When a Jack(son) is played, all ghouls try to be the first to put their hand down on the stack and shout 'Jack Snap'!

5. The first ghoul to put their hand on the stack gets to take it and add it to the bottom of her own pile of cards.

6. The ghoul to the left of the Jack-Snapper starts a new pile in the centre of the table.

7. The game ends when one ghoul gets all the cards.

RULES:

⛧ If a ghoul loses all her cards, she has one chance to get back in the game. The next time a Jack(son) is played, if she's the first to put her hand down, she's back in. If she isn't, then she's officially out.

⛧ If multiple ghouls put their hands on the Jack(son), the ghoul with her hand at the bottom gets the cards. No using claws, ghouls!

⛧ If a ghoul puts her hand down on a card that isn't a Jack(son), she has to give the ghoul who played that card one of the cards from her own pile.

Deal the entire deck of cards.
For this game, you do need to look
at your cards. Sort your hand into
sequences of each suit.

1. The ghoul with the seven of diamonds starts by placing this card in the middle, face up. The game continues with each ghoul, if possible, adding a diamond card to the sequence. The sequence can either go up (eight, nine, ten and so on) or down (six, five, four and so on).

2. These cards are placed on either side of the seven on the table, in order, so the diamonds form a row.

3. If you don't have the correct diamond card, you can start a new sequence in a different suit by placing any other seven below the seven of diamonds, starting a new row for that suit. If you don't have the correct diamond or another seven, you skip your turn.

4. The winner is the first ghoul to use up all of her cards, although the remaining ghouls can continue until all four rows are complete.

Give yourself five points every time you win a round of Jack(son) Snap or Scary Sevens. Keep track of your scores to see who's the most skilled card spark!

Ghoul Name					
Round one					
Round two					
Round three					
Round four					
Round five					
Round six					
Round seven					
Round eight					
Round nine					
Round ten					
Totals					

FREAKY FAB

Ghoul Name					
Round one					
Round two					
Round three					
Round four					
Round five					
Round six					
Round seven					
Round eight					
Round nine					
Round ten					
Totals					

SCREAM TEAM

Party Review: Freaky-Fab Events

What special boo-casions did you skelebrate? What special boo-nique touches did you add to make the party your own? What would you do differently next time? Write all about it here!

GHOUL NERD

For Your Ghoul-friends

Ghoulfriends are forever! You always need to have your ghouls' backs and that includes throwing parties for them to skelebrate the end of exams, to help them update their wardrobes or just because you think a party would make their weekend. That's what ghoulfriends are for!

PRETTY SCARY T-SHIRT PARTY

If you've never used your creative fires to design your own clothes, now is the time to start. Ask your ghoulfriends to each bring a T-shirt to decorate. Cover your table with paper tablecloths (dab some artful paint blobs on them) and set out a stack of palettes and some jars of paintbrushes. Don't forget snacks — 'starving artist' is a cliché you can live without!

You'll need:

- ★ T-shirts (plain white shirts or shirts with colours or patterns – whichever you want!)
- ★ fabric pens
- ★ thread
- ★ sewing needles
- ★ scissors
- ★ tape measure
- ★ embellishments of your choice

You'll use the tape measure and fabric pens to mark where you want to cut, paint or add embellishments.

DRAGONTASTIC DESIGNS

With a T-shirt and your sewing and craft supplies you'll have a freaky-fab designer piece that is 100 per cent you. But before you put your claws on any fabric, you need to work out what you want to make. Using pencil and paper, draw some T-shirt design ideas.

Design tips:

- Remember that you can use scissors to cut the neck, cuffs and bottom of your shirt into different shapes.

- Try a simple pattern, like a brightly coloured straight line down the centre of the shirt or something more complex like squiggles everyscare!

- Add some embellishments! You can try buttons, ribbons, lace, fabric patches, embroidery, acrylic paint, plaited fabric and more.

DRAW SOME OF YOUR IDEAS HERE

CLAWARD CEREMONY

After you finish your monsterpieces, show off your creations and vote for some clawsome awards. Give the awards below and include some award ideas of your own.

★ Most Boo-nique
★ Spookiest Style
★ Most Skelegant

★ Beast All-Around
★ Beast Effort

International Ghouls of Mystery Party

I GOT MAD SKILLS

Sometimes a ghoul's got some spying to do and she doesn't want anyone to know about it. A spooky spy party is a great place to learn how to snoop around. Decorate with some incognito black and white, add some spy silhouettes to the walls and prep a table with spy supplies for your ghoulfriends — oversized sunglasses, magnifying glasses and notepads with mini pens.

SO THIS CENTURY...

GHOULS IN DISGUISE

The first step to being a spy is learning to go undercover. Trench coats are old hat, of course, but a ghoul needs to have some other options up her fins, so I always like to make monsterstaches!

You'll need:

★ black, brown, red and yellow felt
★ tracing paper
★ scissors
★ pencils
★ permanent markers
★ glue
★ straws
★ sequins and glitter (optional)

1. Draw the monsterstache of your choice and cut out the monsterstache shape from your tracing paper.

2. Using the tracing paper as a stencil, draw the monsterstache shape onto your felt with a permanent marker pen.

3. Cut out your monsterstache.

4. If you want your disguise to have a sparkly spirit, glue sequins or glitter to your 'tache.

5. Glue the straw to the back of your monsterstache as a handle (on the right side if you're right-handed and on the left side if you're left-handed.)

NOW YOU HAVE AN INSTANT SPOOKY DISGUISE!

CREEP A SECRET

All spies have to communicate in code,
of course, to protect their secrets.
And you can never learn too many codes!
Check this one out.

Write your message backwards:

!edoc retsnom terces ym si sihT

But that isn't disguised very well, so add
one random letter and one random number
before each character, like this:

!x7ek2dj7ot6cm9
rd1ew3tl8sh7nd4ob2md5
tv7ea4rf6cr3eb9sq1 yv6mg8
sp7ih4 sm9iz2hr6Tf1

The message is "This is my secret monster code!"

Now write some secret
messages to your ghoulfriends!

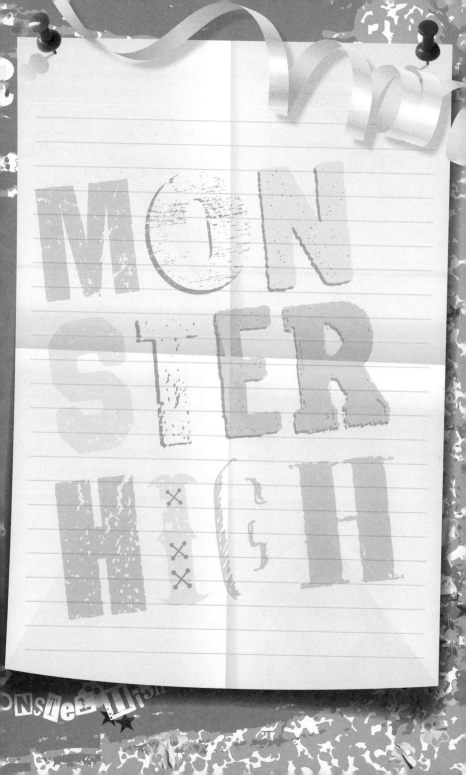

PASSING SECRET MESSAGES

GHOUL NERd

Now that you have secret messages to give to one another, you have to work out how to transfer them without getting caught. Eat some snacks, gossip and try out one another's monsterstaches — and try to pass your message to your spy partner without anyone else noticing (you'll want to fold it up very small, so it's hard for anyone to see).

Can you pass your message without anyone finding out?

My BESTIE

HERE ARE SOME MONSTER METHODS TO TRY:

👁 Make eye contact with your asset when no one else is looking so that she knows you're trying to get the message to her.

👁 Hand your contact a snack, a hairband or an iCoffin — along with the message, hidden in your palm.

👁 Put the message in between the pages of a magazine, book or newspaper and put it down somewhere. Make sure your asset sees you doing it, but act casual.

👁 When your asset is looking at you, drop something (along with the message) and let her pick it up for you. Try to make it seem like an accident!

WHAT ARE SOME OTHER TRICKS YOU CAN TRY?

After every ghoul has passed her message (or been caught trying), it's time to decode them and read them out loud!

GUESS THE GHOUL

Identifying clues is a key part of both spying and journalism. Can you recognize clues that your ghoulfriends leave behind?

YOU'LL NEED:
★ white paper
★ pink marker
★ pencil

Instructions:

1. With the marker, trace your left hand (even if you're left-handed) on a sheet of paper. Everyone needs to share the same marker so the colour will be identical!

2. Write your name in pencil on the back of your sheet.

3. Gather all the sheets together and mix them up. Spread the sheets out on a table or the floor or hang them on the wall. Number the sheets.

4. Now, on another sheet of paper, write down who you think each hand belongs to.

5. Once everyone has guessed, turn the hand outlines over to see which hand goes with which ghoul!

SKE-LASER COURSE

It's definitely worth sneaking something out of a museum to thwart a villain's wicked plan to steal it! So can you make it through the ske-laser field without touching any lasers?

In a hallway, tape hot-pink crêpe paper or wool in a laser pattern, like the one below. Each ghoul has three minutes to get through the ske-laser field without touching any ske-lasers.

For Your Ghoulfriends: Party Review

What party did you throw for your ghoulfriends? And what would be the ultimate dream party to throw for (or with!) them?

MONSTER HIGH